LAGOON BOOKS

Puzzle Compilation: Jenny Lynch
Design & Illustration: Linley Clode
Cover Design: James Davies
Editors: Nick Hoare and Simon Melhuish

Published by:
LAGOON BOOKS
PO BOX 311, KT2 5QW, U.K.
CE Keep address for future reference

ISBN 1 89971 206 2

MIND-BENDING

LATERAL THINKING

PUZZLES

All the Mind-Bending Puzzle books have been carefully compiled to give the reader a refreshingly wide range of challenges, some requiring only a small leap of perception, others deep and detailed thought. All four books share an eye-catching and distinctive visual style that presents each problem in an appealing and intriguing way. Do not, however, be deceived; what is easy on the eye is not necessarily easy on the mind!

Aman stood looking through the window on the forty-fourth floor of an office block. Suddenly, he was seized by an irrational impulse. He wrenched the window open and jumped through it. Though it was a sheer drop to the bottom, the man escaped unhurt. He did not use a parachute or land on any particularly soft surface. Can you explain this?

A car with faulty brakes was approaching a level crossing at 75 miles an hour. A train was approaching the same crossing at 75 miles an hour. The train was 300 ft long and it was 150ft from the crossing. The car was 150 ft from the crossing. Neither car nor train stopped, swerved or changed speed. The crossing was unmanned and without barriers. Yet there was no collision. How is this?

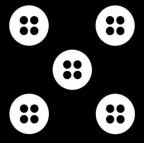

A carrot, a football scarf and five buttons were found lying on the lawn. If nobody put them on the lawn, how did they get there?

Sarah's grandmother is younger than her mother. How is this possible?

A woman watched her husband plunge head first down a deep ravine. She returned home to find him in the kitchen, chopping onions. How is this possible?

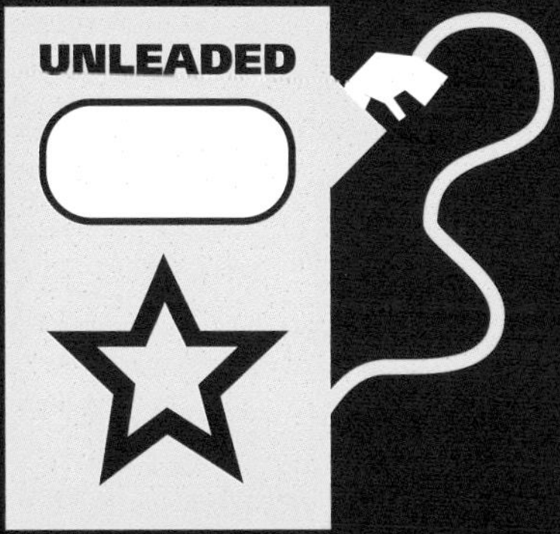

One morning a petrol station attendant ran into the office the moment his boss arrived, and told him that the previous evening he had dreamt that one of the pumps had been leaking, causing a huge explosion. His boss was sceptical, but when he checked the pump in question, he indeed found a potentially-disastrous leak. He switched off the pump, and then sacked the attendant. Why?

On the table is a carton containing six eggs. Six people enter the room and each takes an egg, yet one egg remains in the carton. How is this possible?

When asked who a certain photograph was of, the owner replied "Uncles and brothers have I none, but that man's father is my father's son". Who was in the photograph?

How many animals of each species did Moses take on the ark?

A man stopped his car opposite a hotel and immediately knew that he was bankrupt. How?

A man returned his soup to the restaurant kitchen because there was a dead fly floating in it. When the waiter returned with a new bowl of soup, the diner was incensed to discover that it was exactly the same soup, simply with the fly removed. How did he know?

A woodcutter had some wood. Initially it was in the shape of a pyramid, then he changed it into a cube, and then into the shape of a rectangle. These shapes never got any smaller however, and the woodcutter never actually cut the wood. How did he do this?

A woman owned

a vase worth

£5000, yet she

deliberately

smashed it.

Why?

In a deserted barn, a dead man is found hanging from a central rafter, with a wet patch underneath him. The rope around his neck is five feet long and his feet are four feet off the ground. The walls are fifteen feet away. There is nothing else in the building, no ladders or boxes. How did the man manage to hang himself?

A man walked into a bar, put £1 on the table and asked for half a pint of lager. The barmaid asked whether he would like Kronenburg or Fosters. He asked for Kronenburg. A little later, another man entered the bar, put £1 on the table and asked for half a pint of lager. She immediately pulled him half a pint of Kronenburg. Why?

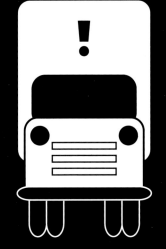

A lorry attempted to drive under a low bridge but got caught underneath it. People stopped and tried to help the driver free his vehicle, but they couldn't push it either forwards or backwards. What is the solution?

Two Scrabble champions played five games of Scrabble. Each won and lost the same number of games and there were no draws. How is this possible?

A bookworm chewed its way through a three volume encyclopedia set. If the covers of each volume are 2.5mm thick and the pages 310mm thick, how far did the worm travel, as it made its way from the first page of volume one to the last page of volume three.

Simon and Robert were brothers. Simon married Mandy. Robert married Dawn. Simon and Dawn shared the same wedding anniversary but Robert's anniversary was six months before this date and Mandy's was three months after it. None of them got divorced or remarried, so how is this possible?

Add 2 to 171 and make it less than eighteen.

Every morning a woman takes the lift from her apartment on the twelfth floor, leaves the building and goes off to work. When she returns in the evening however, the woman always gets out of the lift on the eighth floor and walks up the remaining stairs to her flat. She was not a keep-fit fanatic so why did she do this?

You enter a deserted house late at night. Inside there is an oil lamp, a gas fire and a stove full of wood. You have only one match however, so which should you light first?

A man was returning home after having drunk a great deal. He was walking in the middle of the road and was dressed all in black. There were no streetlights and no moonlight. A car with no headlights on came racing towards him. The car managed to swerve just in time to avoid the man. How did the driver know he was there?

A **B** **C**

D **E** **F**

G **H** **I**

J **K** **L**

M **N** **O**

The five pieces of chain need to be linked to form one continuous length. One method is to open link C (one move), fasten it to link D (two moves), open link F etc. This will take eight moves. Can you do it in less?

A boy was twelve years old on his second birthday. How is this so?

Mr Robinson wanted a house where the windows in all of the rooms faced south. How did he manage this?

Two fathers and two sons enter a shop and spend £1.50 each. The shopkeeper takes £4.50. What happened to the rest?

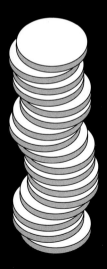

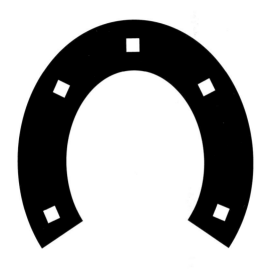

A horse ploughs a field all day. If he takes twenty four steps to reach from one edge of the field to the other, how many hoof prints will the horse leave in the last furrow?

Why are

1989 pennies

worth

more

than

1982 pennies?

A snail crawls slowly up a garden wall 48 cm high. If it crawls forward 8 cm a day and slips back 3cm each night, how long will it take to reach the top of the wall?

A stranger entered a bar and asked the barman for a glass of water. The barman pulled a gun out from under the bar and pointed it at him. The stranger thanked the barman and left, not having had the water he asked for. Why?

A traveller set out on a journey and stopped only when he had returned to his starting point. During that journey, his head travelled 36 feet further than his feet, yet his feet remained attached to his body. What is the explanation for this?

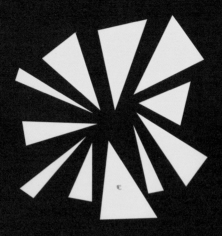

Antony and Cleopatra were found dead in the bedroom. The window was open and broken glass was found on the floor. There were no marks on their bodies, they had not been poisoned and there was not a single person in the house when they died. What had happened?

The lights suddenly went out as the woman was halfway down the stairs. She knew immediately that her husband had died. How?

An airplane full of Mexicans crashed and landed directly on the border between Colombia and Venezuela. Where should the survivors be buried?

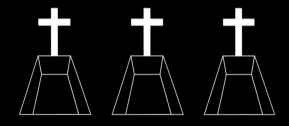

A man had lived alone for three years, during which time no-one came to visit him and he never went out. One night he decided that he had had enough. He put the fire out, turned off the lights, put on his coat and went out for a walk. He was never seen or heard of again. Inconsequential though his action may seem, it resulted in the deaths of nine people. Why?

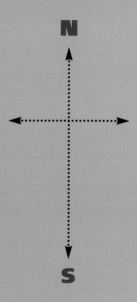

Two guardsman were on guard duty. One faced up the road to watch anyone approaching from the north and the other looked down the road to watch anyone approaching from the south. "You look a bit rough this morning" said one of them to the other. How did he know?

When a boat is at anchor, five of the rungs on the rope ladder over its side are underwater. If the rungs are 30cm apart and each one is 3 cm thick, how many rungs would be underwater four hours later, if the tide rises at 35cm per hour?

In order to improve road safety, a law was passed making the wearing of seat belts compulsory. The number of road accidents remained exactly the same and the local hospital was even more busy than before in dealing with road accident victims. Why?

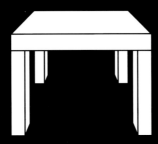

Two men are seated at a table. Neither has spoken for one and a half hours. There is no-one else in the room. Suddenly, one of them shouts with glee and leaps up before collapsing with an agonised yell. What has happened?

Ｈow many mice are there in the room if there is a mouse in each of the four corners, and opposite each mouse there are three mice and at each mouse's tail there is a mouse?

A woman has to cut a roll of ribbon into one metre lengths. If it takes her two seconds to measure and cut a length and the whole roll is fifty metres long, how long will it take her to do it?

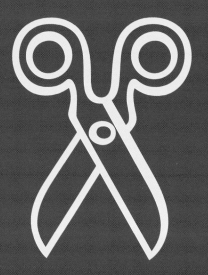

P olice broke into a house to find the owner slumped dead across an armchair with a bullet hole in his neck. By his side lay a gun and a cassette recorder. When one of the officers pushed the start button on the machine they heard the following message, "Sorry but I cannot go on any longer. Suicide seems the only way out." There followed the noise of a gunshot. Why did the police immediately assume that they had a murder investigation on their hands?

Two children had just finished playing in the cellar. The face of one was covered with dust but the other one's face remained quite clean. Yet it was the child with the clean face who went to wash himself. Why is this?

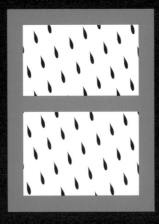

Five men were travelling along a lane. It began to rain. Four of the men quickened their step and got wet. The fifth man did not quicken his step but remained quite dry. He did not have an umbrella or hat. How can this be?

A woman is out shopping. At one point, she stops, searches in her bag for a coin, and puts it in a slot. She sighs and begins to search for another coin. Suddenly she stops, takes off her coat, and then deposits the second coin. Thoroughly disgruntled, she puts her coat back on and walks away. What has just happened?

Mr and Mrs Pilsbury were fit, healthy people in the prime of their lives. Their neighbour, Miss Holden, was a frail old woman, arthritic and hard of hearing. Yet one day, they invited her round to their house to do something which neither of them could do. She had no special skill which they didn't possess, so why did they need her?

When is

it more

polite to

pass or

overtake

on the

inside?

YELLOW?

Polly Warden loved the colour yellow. All the walls in her new bungalow were primrose yellow. The carpets, curtains and all the soft furnishings were a golden yellow. What colour were her stairs?

Hugh and Steven were professional golfers and were very competitive. During one game, they had each scored thirty when Steven made a very bad shot. Hugh immediately added ten to his score. Hugh then hit an excellent shot and declared that he had won the game. How is this possible?

A doctor and police surgeon were comparing notes on a case. The doctor explained that a man had fallen asleep whilst at the cinema. The horror film he had been watching obviously influenced his dream. He dreamt that he was being chased through a deserted castle by a beast with two heads. He ran to the top of a tower and found himself looking down a fifty foot drop into a crocodile-infested moat. Behind him he could hear the beast's roar as it made its way up the stairs towards him. Just as he had to turn and face the beast, his wife shook him to waken him. The shock was so great for the poor man that he immediately collapsed and died.

"That's absolute nonsense", cried the surgeon.

How was he so sure?

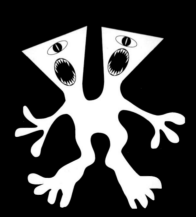

A father and son were involved in a car accident and rushed to hospital. On seeing the unconscious young boy, the surgeon exclaimed, "Oh no, that's my son". How can this be true?

A man enters a house. There is no other person inside. He goes into one of the rooms and suddenly puts his hands in the air. Then he lets them drop, laughs and leaves. Can you explain this?

A man leapt out of an aeroplane unhurt, though he had no parachute. What happened?

The maker does not need it, the buyer does not use it and the user uses it without knowing. What is it?

How can someone be
39 years old in 1990
but only 35 in 1994?

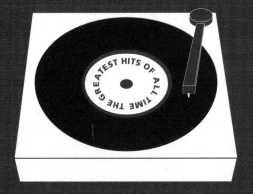

A vinyl record measures 32cm across. There is a 1cm margin round the edge and a centre label which measures 10 cm across. There are 30 grooves per cm. How far does a needle travel if the record is played from start to finish?

An off-duty detective clearly heard the words "For God's sake, Mark, don't shoot" as he walked past a building. As he raced to where he heard the words come from, he heard a single gunshot ring out. He entered a room to find a dead woman on the floor and, beside the body, a postman, a plumber and an electrical engineer. The detective looked at each in turn before deciding to arrest the postman for the murder. How did he know?

The scene was set for confrontation one night, as rival mafia gangs made reservations at the same restaurant. At one point, a member of Luigi's gang marched up to a member of Roberto's gang and thumped him hard on the back. The poor man fell to the floor. Then he rose, looked at the man who struck him, thanked him and walked quietly away. Why?

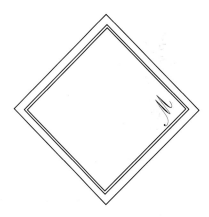

A man and a woman were sitting alone in a train compartment, on their journey home. The woman decided to go to the buffet car but on her return, found that the man had leapt to his death out of the train. He left nothing behind him except a large handkerchief. The woman was distraught, knowing that if they had picked any other form of transport, he would not have committed suicide. What happened?

A man died on January 23rd yet was buried on January 22nd. Why the premature burial?

A woman was being chased through the jungle by a tribe of hunters. She had in her possession two solid gold ingots which weighed 9lbs each. She came to a rope bridge which she needed to cross, but which she knew could only support 125lbs in weight. She herself weighed 110lbs. She did not have time to carry the ingots across one at a time and it was too far to throw them. She did not have any shoes which she could remove, and the hunters were getting closer with every second, so how can she escape with both gold ingots?

If Lady Arbuthnot's peacock laid an egg in Lady Fawcett's garden, who is the rightful owner of the egg?

A hijacker with a plane load of hostages radioed his ransom demands to ground control. He asked for £500,000 and two parachutes in return for the safe return of the hostages. These were duly brought on board and the hijacker ordered the pilot to take off and fly towards the original destination. When they were flying over a barren landscape, the hijacker parachuted to safety, taking all the money and was never seen, or heard of, again. So why did he request two parachutes?

This

sentance

containes

two

misstakes.

How many mistakes are there in the sentence above?

How many grooves are there on a long playing record, 30cm in diameter, with a 10cm label in the centre and a 1cm margin on the outside?

LONGEST LONG-PLAYING LP OF ALL TIME

A woman had just moved to a new area and needed some dental work done. There were two dentists in the town and she visited them both. The first had a brand new surgery, he looked very well-presented and good-tempered and had excellent teeth himself. The second had very bad teeth, a rather untidy surgery and was constantly in a bad mood caused by chronic toothache. So why did the woman decide to register with the second dentist?

The king of Flotsia was a very tyrannical man who had decided that none of his subjects were to leave his kingdom. In addition, the entry of any foreigners was to be tightly controlled. The border between Flotsia and its neighbour, Jetsia, was a footbridge spanning a deep gorge. A guard was posted there and ordered to shoot on sight anyone he saw trying to escape across the bridge, out of Flotsia. Anybody trying to cross in the opposite direction, from Jetsia into Flotsia, had to have authorisation papers otherwise they were ordered to turn round. He sat in his hut on the Flotsia side of the bridge and came out to look every five minutes.

If it takes between 9 – 10 minutes to get across the bridge and there is no place to hide once you are on it, how did a Flotsian woman manage to escape across the bridge, into Jetsia, without having to harm or incapacitate the guard?

A woman parked her car outside the bank and ran inside. She held up 15 people and ran outside with £10,000 in cash. A policeman saw her and stopped her. He told her off but then let her go. Why?

A dead man was found inside a caravan. He had shot himself. Next to his body, the police found a block of wood. The wood was approximately two foot in length and had no markings on it, yet the police were sure that this piece of wood led directly to the man committing suicide. How are they linked?

Can a man marry his widow's...

SISTER?

If a man cannot be tried for the same crime twice, why was Edward Dukes tried six times last week for the murder of Lady Soames?

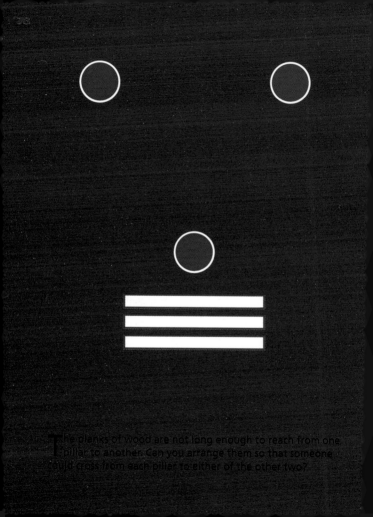

The planks of wood are not long enough to reach from one pillar to another. Can you arrange them so that someone could cross from each pillar to either of the other two?

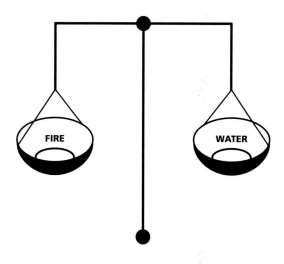

A man was found guilty of libel. The king decreed that the man should decide his own fate by making a single statement. If the statement were true, the man would be burnt at the stake. If the statement were false, the man would be thrown out to sea. What did the clever man say which resulted in him being freed?

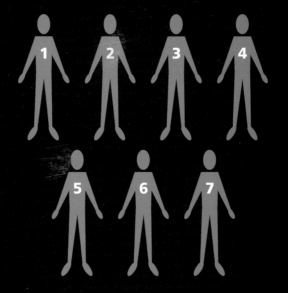

A group of seven people arrived at a hotel late one night and asked for seven rooms. The hotelier actually only had six rooms available but said he would try and help. He put the first person in the first room and asked the second to wait a moment. Then he placed the third person in the second room, the fourth in the third room and the fifth in the fourth room. Finally he placed the sixth in the fifth room and went back for the seventh person, whom he placed in the sixth room. Satisfied?

A girl asked her parents if she could go to an all-night party. They agreed as long as she was back before sunrise. Imagine their surprise when they saw her return, a stone heavier in weight and with long hair. What had happened?

Two men are lying in the ditch in the countryside, next to a parked van. One of the men is dead, the other is in convulsions, sobbing hysterically. Both have uniforms on – but they are not the same. What has just happened?

Two men and a woman were stuck in a lift during a heatwave. One of the men had three bottles of mineral water with him and the other had five. They shared the eight bottles of water equally between the three of them. Once they had been freed, the woman gave the men eight coins as payment. What is the fairest method of dividing the eight coins?

A man lies dead in a field. Next to him is an unopened package. There is nobody else around. How did he die?

What is the next letter in this series?

OTTFFS

Page 6

The man was a window cleaner, so he started off outside the building and actually jumped into it.

Page 7

The car was on the train, being transported.

Page 8

They are the remains of a snowman after a thaw.

Page 9

It is quite possible that her paternal grandmother could be younger than her mother. If her mother is 58 and her father 24, her father's mother could be 44.

Page 10

Her husband was a stuntman and she had been watching him at work.

Page 11

The attendant had been on the night shift, and should not have been asleep!

Page 12

The last person took the last egg, still in its carton!

Page 13

It was the owner's son.

Page 14

None. It was Noah's ark.

Page 15

He was playing Monopoly.

Page 16

He had seasoned the soup with lots of pepper before seeing the dead fly.

Page 17

The wood was sawdust which he poured into appropriately shaped containers.

Page 18

She owned another identical one and wished to increase its value by making it unique.

Page 19

He stood on a block of ice until it melted.

Page 20

The tariff displays two different prices, Kronenburg is £1 per half and Fosters is 90p. The first man put a one pound coin on the table (so may have required some change depending on his choice of lager), the second put down a fifty pence piece, two twenties and a ten.

Page 21

If they let some air out of the tyres, then they will be able to push the vehicle free.

Page 22

They were not playing each other.

Page 23

If you look at the illustration you will see that if the worm starts at page one of volume of volume one, it will eat through the front cover of volume one (2.5mm), the back cover of volume two (2.5mm), the pages of volume two (310mm), the front cover of volume two (2.5mm) and the back cover of volume three (2.5mm). The worm is now at the last page of volume three. Total distance travelled is 320mm.

Page 24

Simon and Robert are clergyman. Robert married Simon to Mandy which is why they share the same wedding anniversary. Simon married Dawn to her husband and Robert to his wife.

page 25

17 $^1/_2$

Page 26

She was a midget and could not reach the button for the twelfth floor.

Page 27

The match.

Page 28

It was midday, so the driver saw him.

Page 29

Unfasten links a, b, and c, and use them to link the remaining four lengths together. This will take only six moves.

Page 30

He was born on 29th February 1896. The year 1900 was not a leap year (1900 is not divisible by 400) so the next February 29 does not occur until 1904.

Thus he would actually be eight years old on his second birthday and twelve years old by the time his third birthday occurred.

Page 31

He built a house on the North Pole so that all four sides faced south.

Page 32

Only three men entered the shop, a son, father and grandfather, so only £4.50 was spent.

Page 33

None. The plough will turn the soil over and cover any hoof prints left by the animal.

Page 34

Because there are seven more of them. It is easy to assume that the numbers are dates rather than quantities.

Page 35

Nine days. If it travels 8 cm forward and 3 cm back during each twenty four hours than it is progressing at the rate of 5 cm per day. After eight days it will be 40 cm up the wall, so on the ninth day it will reach the top.

Page 36

The stranger was suffering from hiccups, which is why he asked for some water. The barman realised this and drew the gun in order to give the man a shock. This worked, the man was cured of his hiccups and, no longer needing the water, left.

Page 37

The journey was right round the globe. The man's head was six feet from the ground so the radius of the circle travelled by his head is six feet greater than the circle travelled by his feet. The difference in the circumferences of the circles is 2 (pi) x 6 = 36.

Page 38

Anthony and Cleopatra were goldfish whose bowl was knocked over by an intruding dog. They died from asphyxiation.

Page 39

She was leaving the hospital and her husband was in intensive care. The power failure that caused the lights to go out, meant that her husband's life support machine stopped working.

Page 40

You do not bury survivors.

Page 41

He was a lighthouse keeper. When he turned out the light, a shipwreck occurred.

Page 42

They were facing each other.

Page 43

Five. The boat is afloat, so as the tide rises, so does the boat!

Page 44

The new law reduced the number of deaths from road accidents, but there were now a greater number of survivors with injuries who needed treatment.

Page 45

The two men were intent on a game of chess. Having finally achieved "Check-mate", one of them leapt to his feet in glee – only to discover that his leg had gone completely dead whilst he was playing.

Page 46

Four mice, each one near the tail of the mouse in the adjacent corner.

Page 47

98 seconds.

The last cut separates two lengths so only 49 cuts are needed to get fifty lengths of ribbon.

Page 48

Because the tape was already rewound, ready for them to listen to.

Page 49

They looked at each other! The clean child saw the other's dirty face and assumed that he was as dirty. The child who was dirty only saw the other's clean face so had no reason to think that he was not also clean himself.

Page 50

The four men were pall bearers and the fifth was the corpse in the coffin.

Page 51

The woman stepped on a weighing machine in a chemist's. She removed her coat to try and make herself weigh less – but it did not work.

Page 52

They needed her to act as a witness while they signed a document.

Page 53

On a spiral staircase where the insides are narrower and hence harder to climb.

Page 54

There are no stairs in a bungalow.

Page 55

They were playing tennis.

Page 56

If the man died so quickly, no-one could possibly know what he had been dreaming of.

Page 57

The surgeon was the boy's mother.

Page 58

The man was a burglar who raised his hands on hearing the words "Stop, thief". When he realised that these words were uttered by a pet parrot in a cage, he relaxed, laughed and made a hasty retreat.

Page 59

The aeroplane was on the ground when he leapt.

Page 60

A coffin

Page 61

If they were born in the years BC, it would be true.

Page 62

Just over 10cm. The number of grooves per cm is not relevant as the needle does not go round the record, the record turns and the needle travels from the outside edge to the centre. Because it follows a slightly curved path, the distance would be slightly more than 10cm exactly.

Page 63

The plumber and electrical engineer were women, so only the postman could be "Mark".

Page 64

Roberto's gang member had a fish bone stuck in his throat. The thump on the back was to help clear it.

Page 65

The man had been treated for blindness and was wearing the hand-kerchief as a blindfold, to protect his eyes. When alone, he could not resist removing it, in order to check his new-found sight. Unfortunately, the train was going through a tunnel at that moment and the man could see only darkness. Full of despair, thinking that he was still blind, the man jumped out of the train.

Page 66

The man died in Fiji and the body was flown to Western Samoa for burial. Such a flight would cross the International Date Line from West to East and in effect, the date would go back one day.

Page 67

She walked across, juggling the ingots.

Page 68

Peacocks do not lay eggs.

Page 69

If they thought that he was going to take a hostage with him then they had to give him good parachutes. If he asked for just one, they could have sent him a faulty one.

Page 70

Four - three spelling mistakes plus the mistaken claim that it contains only two mistakes.

Page 71

Two – one on each side.

Page 72

If there are only two dentists in town, the woman deduced that they must treat each other's teeth. Therefore the dentist with bad teeth had treated and looked after the dentist with good teeth.

Page 73

When he was in his hut, the woman started to walk across the bridge. She walked for nearly five minutes and then turned round and started to walk back towards Flotsia. When she reached the guard, she had no papers to show him, so he made her turn round and return to Jetsia!

Page 74

She had parked on double yellow lines, so the policeman was giving her a warning about that.

Page 75

The man was a midget in a local circus. He measured himself against the wood every day.

An envious rival had chopped two inches off the wood that morning so that the midget believed he had grown and was no longer the world's smallest man. Desolate at losing his livelihood, the man committed suicide.

Page 76

No, because he would have to be dead in order to have a widow.

Page 77

Edward was an actor in an amateur dramatic society's annual Agatha Christie production.

Page 78

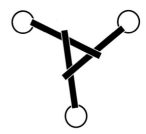

Page 79

One went through at 8.00am and the other at 9.00am.

Page 80

When the man originally parked his car, he removed the parking ticket from another car and put it on his own windscreen. This meant that the warden never actually issued a ticket for his car so the man could drive away without being prosecuted.

Page 81

He said "I will be thrown out to sea." If the king did throw him out to sea then that statement will have been true, so he should have burnt him instead. But if he did burn him, then that statement would have been false. The king had no alternative but to let him go.

Page 82

The second person still does not have a room.

Page 83

It was a very long party! The events took place in Northern Alaska in the middle of November, when the sun sets and does not rise again for 65 days.

Page 84

The two men are a prisoner and a prison officer, handcuffed together. The prisoner had made an attempt to escape during a road-side stop. the guard put the key in his mouth while he tried to restrain the prisoner but, in the ensuing battle, he swallowed it.

Page 85

If there were eight bottles and three people, each person drank two and two thirds of a bottle. So the man who had three bottles gave away one third of a bottle whereas the man with five bottles gave away two and one thirds of a bottle. Thus the second man gave away seven times as much as the first man. The man who had five bottles should receive seven coins and the man with three bottles should receive one coin.

Page 86

The unopened package is his parachute which failed to open.

Page 87

S. They are the initial letters for the numbers one, two, three etc.